D0727569

Quicksilver

A 25th anniversary anthology

Black Isle Writers

www.blackislewriters.org

Bassman Books

Published by Bassman Books, Burnside Cottage,
Newhall, Balblair, Dingwall, IV7 8LT

ISBN 978-0-9567908-5-9

A catalogue record for this book is available from the
British Library

Printed by For The Right Reasons, 60 Grant Street,
Inverness, IV3 8BS

Layout and design by Russell Turner
www.russellturner.org

Set in Palatino 11/13pt

Black Isle Writers
Charity No SCO 23701

Contents

Workshops: Memoirs

Workshops: Humour

Foreword

Quicksilver is the Silver Anniversary Anthology of the Black Isle Writers, written and edited by current members.

Some of the pieces were written for a competition or in preparation for a workshop, others during a workshop. Like quicksilver, words often flow on to the page in an unpredictable stream and have to be coalesced through thoughtful editing into the shining finished article.

Some of the contributions in *Quicksilver* are light-hearted, others more thought-provoking. Whatever your taste, we hope you find lots to enjoy.

The main aim of The Black Isle Writers is to encourage and support the creative writing of our members. Several of our current members are published writers and competition winners.

The group originated as an extramural evening class in creative writing tutored by Rosemarkie author Elizabeth Sutherland. When Highland Regional Council ceased to run the class, six of the participants wanted to continue to meet. They called themselves The Black Isle Writers Group and Elizabeth was its first Chair.

Since reaching a high of forty, membership numbers have stabilised at what we feel is the optimum of around twenty. This number makes for rich and friendly meetings.

We meet twice a month from September until May, following a varied programme of practical creative writing workshops, outside speakers and opportunities to share our writing with other members.

In addition to the main programme, the Group has organised one-day events. Especially successful was *A Criminal Event*, held in June 1995, attended by 139 would-be crime writers. It featured inputs by crime writer PD James, forensic scientist Ros Brown from Grampian Police, Dingwall-based Procurator Fiscal David Hingston, and Superintendent Hugh Mackay, Ross, Cromarty and Skye Area Commander. Alex Gray was one of the delegates who left thinking "I could do that, be a crime writer". She now writes full time.

Eleanore Simpson
Chair, Black Isle Writers 2013-14

Quicksilver

Sheena Munro

There – it said –
there's something for you –
look at it
silver, gleaming, lustrous, refulgent
but silent, motionless?
I want to feel it, to listen, to smell, to taste its beauty
Quicksilver – living metal –
silver – mooncolour
mysterious, full of secrets
see the life trembling there –
a slave waiting to be captured
but one touch and it will metamorphose,
escape in a thousand laughing fragments
quicksilver – a poem in an oxymoron.

Divine Retribution

Lynn Valentine
Winner of the 2014 BIW writing competition
on the theme Redemption or Retribution

The world watched as they killed my family. The world wrung its hands as they killed my village. The world hung its head as they killed my country. I am twenty years older now but not any wiser.

There were one hundred days of killing in Rwanda in 1994. No-one knows how many died. I would say a million but there are four out of that million that I grieve more than others.

I lived in a village called Nyamiga. You will not have heard of it. You will not find it on your Google street view. So I will tell it to you.

Our nearest city was Butare. We would go there to the markets to sell our produce. It took half a day to walk to the city, half a day to sell our produce and half a day to walk back to our home. We would set off early pushing carts to the market and return late. Our goodbyes and welcomes in Nyamiga were always done in the dark.

Although I was young and full of energy, these journeys took their toll and I had little interest in the city then. No time to visit the grand Cathedral or the Museum. Only time to set up our stall and sell as much as I could. My Mother said I was the best at getting a fair price.

Our village life centred round our farming and the Catholic Church. Our church was a very small place, only room enough for fifty people or so but we would squeeze in to hear Father Mukankundiye preach. He preached at many places but we were honoured to have him live at our village. He was truly 'our' priest, belonging to us more than he did to the other villages. It was him that had taught me to read and write. Now I did the same for others when I could, using the church building as a school for the children of the parish.

I lived with my parents, brother and sister in a small one-storey house with clay walls and a corrugated tin roof. My sister Immacule would be married soon and out of the house but my brother Celestin would stay to help run the farm. I could not ever imagine leaving home, not even for a husband. I loved Nyamiga and everyone who lived in it.

My family and everyone else in the village were all Tutsi. When I was a child this did not matter. As I reached twenty this would be what defined me. I was no longer a farmer's daughter or a teacher or a neighbour. I was Tutsi, a cockroach, and I would be killed.

When the murders started in the North we were afraid but we never thought that the South would succumb to this. We avoided Butare, scared of mixing with Hutus. But we had Hutu neighbours in the next village and the village next to that. Who would save us?

Cyendajura was next to Nyamiga. We heard its screams one morning. Father Mukankundiye rounded us up as a shepherd would his flock. He kept urging us to "hurry, hurry" as he led us to the church. My Mother was stumbling and crying but I dragged her along. Surely God would give us sanctuary. We reached the church as Cyendajura's cries carried on into the day.

Father Mukankundiye was calm, "Be not afraid of them; for the Lord thy God is with thee."

But we were afraid, we were all crying, even the men. We waited for hours, waiting for death to come, willing it to be quick. Father Mukankundiye led us in prayer though most of us could not speak for fear of the Hutus.

And then they were in Nyamiga. We could hear them setting fire to our homes, laughing as they destroyed everything we owned on their way to the church.

But then Father Mukankundiye did a strange thing. He left the church and stood waiting for the Hutus outside while we cowered on the floor of the building waiting for the machetes to fall. We could hear him bargaining with them. A low litany of pleases and thank yous as he made whatever case he could.

But it was not enough. Grenades were thrown into the church as we cowered and screamed. I scrambled at the back as body parts were thrown into the air. Out, out, into the air, running and running away from the village. Behind me I could hear the screams of the dying as the explosions blasted the church. No time to grieve, just keep running. I kept running for hours until I reached the marsh.

The marsh was urunfunzo – papyrus trees. I slathered the mud over me and hid. I heard the killers go by many times over that month but always I stayed in the mud, hiding from them, trying not to think of my dead family.

I lived on beetles, snakes and whatever else I could get. The mosquitos lived on me, better that than the killers. Other Tutsi joined me in the marshes. The Hutus knew we were there and tried to catch us or trick us into coming out but always I hid in the mud. I was one of the lucky ones who never got caught and never got killed. The Hutus called the Tutsi cockroaches and I was truly one of those insects, surviving anything that crossed its path.

When the RPF came to liberate us we crept out of the mud. The genocide was over. I left my country for a refugee camp in Tanzania, still too scared to return home. I stayed in Tanzania long after the refugees were repatriated. I taught and tried to carve a new life out of air. Only now, twenty years later do I feel I want to return.

And so I am home or near to home in Butare. I am finally visiting the Museum, learning more and more about the genocide. I doubt we will ever heal, no matter how many Gacaca courts and community projects there are.

I blink as a familiar figure comes towards me, older and fatter, but still the same man.

"Father Mukankundiye, is it really you?" He has jeans and a t-shirt on, strange to see him in these clothes, strange to see him at all.

"Treasure, my child, I thought you were killed!" He hugs me but I can feel his body shaking as we hug. And then I know. He wasn't pleading for us to be saved as he stood outside the church all those years ago. He was bargaining for his own life. The pleases and thank yous were for himself. He was not knocked down at the door of the church as I had imagined but probably opened it for the Hutus so they could throw the grenades more accurately.

I try to appear unflustered but my mind is whirring. He may as well have killed my family himself.

"Well Father, this is no place to catch up, will we go and have a tea at the café?" He nods and I lead him along the Museum's corridors to the busy café.

I am level-headed now. I know what I need to do.

We find a table and I say I will go and buy some tea and cake for us both. He looks shaken but is trying to smile. Does he know that I know? I stand in the queue for a while, glancing over to make sure he has not left.

"Well," I frown as I make my way back and sit down beside him, "how on earth did you manage to survive?"

He frowns back at me, mouth working frantically. He mumbles, I hear the word forgiveness but my rage makes me deaf. I take the fork from the cake plate and stab him in the neck, as casually as I would swat a fly. His mouth gapes, confusion in his eyes as he tries to stem the bleeding. He falls to the floor screaming as people run over to help.

"Some cockroaches do deserve to die." I stand over him, my healing done. I have put Nyamiga on the map.

One Small Boy

Pam Macintyre

One small boy, mother in tow,
With fur-lined boots, feet aglow,
Face turned upward, mouth wide open,
Eyes shining bright, but no words spoken,
Gazing in wonder at festive cheer,
Cascades of lights twinkling far and near.
Behind a crowded window with stories to tell,
A tableau of toys weaves a magic spell.
With nose pressed firm against the glass,
What more could a little boy ask?

The rattle of a can
Turns the boy's head.
A tramp stands before him
Filling him with dread.
All ragged and pale,
Two wild eyes staring,
Dirty tattered string
Round the coat the man's wearing.

The boy gasps in horror,
This his first real fright.
He tugs his mother's skirt,
They both stare at the sight.
"Spare something for me,"
They hear the poor man say.
The boy's rooted to the spot
But mother pulls him away.

Many years have passed and fortunes come and go
On a street in the city where festive lights don't glow,
Huddled in a cardboard house to pass the time of day,
Where shoes are filled with paper to keep the cold at bay,
A homeless man waits motionless for the evening round

Of soup and bread to comfort that he may sleep more sound.
And as the snow swirls round him, he recalls a day long past,
A tableau of enchantment, nose pressed firm against the glass,
When his innocent world was shaken as he turned to see
A tramp rattle a can at him, wild-eyed and ragged as he.

A gum-chewer's apologia

Fran Tilbrook
(to be read in the style of Pam Ayres)

I am a masticator:
I have to have me fix
of tasty, minty chewing gum,
you know, the kind that sticks
rock hard to surfaces
when I just spits it out.
Can't see why people moan so much,
call me a litter lout.
Me little blobs of spat-out gum,
how star-like they appear,
competing with the festive tinsel,
bringing Christmas cheer.
For I'm an urban artist, enhancing Inverness:
me 'Jackson Pollock' spatter style
should not be called a mess.
Me aim's to cover Falcon Square,
I'm getting in me stride –
I want to demonstrate to all
my kind of civic pride!

Redemption Song

Russell Turner

Runner-up in the 2014 BIW writing competition

Bob Marley was to blame. Cath and I had been together for six months and I thought we'd learned pretty much everything there was to know about each other – certainly the important stuff – but then the row blew up and it seemed I didn't know her at all.

We'd met on a blind date organised by Johnny. He and Liz were newly married and still in that blissful state where he wanted the whole world to be as happy as he was, especially his divorced best mate who'd learned the hard way that single women over forty are available for a reason. That's how it appeared to me, anyway, and if that sounds bitter I'd got good cause. For far too long the only women I'd met were mad, desperate or just wanted to boast to their friends that they'd had a fireman in their bed. Women can be creeps too. So when Johnny told me that Liz had become friendly with the new maths teacher at Henshaw Tech I didn't jump up and down with excitement at his suggestion of a four-some at Luigi's, however good their meatballs are. Horn-rimmed glasses, tweed skirt and hair in a bun was what came to mind, and I was stupid enough to say so one evening when I'd been invited to The Love Nest for a drink and an opportunity for Liz to dissect my recent dating disasters.

"The trouble with you, Pete, is that you don't give them a chance," she told me. "You got burned by Janice and now you assume that every woman's going to do the same."

"To be fair, Cruella was enough to put anyone off women for life," countered Johnny, coming to my defence like any best mate would. "Emptying the joint bank account is one thing. Using it to run away to Australia with Bruce Almighty is another. A man's entitled to be careful after that."

"I don't disagree." She sipped her shiraz and looked at me assessingly. "But five years is long enough to mope. Cath's a love-ly girl – far better than you deserve – so you could at least make the effort to meet her."

"Although what she'll see in this miserable git is a mystery," Johnny added, then raised his glass in salute. Liz smirked.

"He can be made quite presentable if you get him out of jeans and a T-shirt. He's got all his hair and teeth, his stomach's not bad for a forty-five-year-old and he knows which fork to use if you take him anywhere classy. He even reads books that aren't all murder, car chases and explosions."

"But you love the men who do," Johnny breathed into her ear, provoking a most unwifely blush.

"I'm in the room, you know." The two giggled like naughty children. "OK, I surrender. Introduce me to this paragon of womanhood and I'll do my best not to disgrace you, but if she's another one who's sad, mad or just out for a lad you won't hear the last of it."

Two nights later, more nervous than I'd anticipated, I was seated in Luigi's with Johnny when Liz walked in beside a slim, dark-haired woman in a spectacular red dress, clinging but not over-tight, and shoes Janice would have killed for.

"Bloody hell," Johnny muttered, "you've done well here, mate," then stood to greet them. I followed his example and prayed that the spell wouldn't be broken when she spoke.

It wasn't.

*

I'd never believed in love at first sight. Now I did. Amazingly, so did Cath. Within a week she'd moved from her flat to my house and when we weren't exploring each other's bodies we were learning of each other's past and present, likes and dislikes, hopes and dreams. Then Bob changed everything.

During a hilarious evening spent browsing photo albums we'd been joshing each other about long hair, flared denim, hot pants, platform shoes and the merits of our teenage music heroes. While I'd played air guitar with Yes and Deep Purple, Cath had swooned over David Cassidy and The Sweet. We found some common ground in disco – Barry White for me, Donna Summer for her – then diverged again when punk rock slouched on to the music scene and stuck two fingers up at everyone. I hated the nihilism; she loved the energy. More bands and singers were thrown around until I made a mildly dismissive comment about Bob Marley. She looked as though I'd struck her.

"How can you say that?"

"I just said..."

"I heard you. Bob was... he was..." She shook her head, defeated. When I reached out to touch her she backed away, shook her head again and ran from the room. A moment later, before I'd even moved, I heard her car screech out of the drive and down the road. What the hell had happened?

After ten agonising minutes I was ready to call the police. Then the phone rang.

"She's here." It was Johnny. I'd never heard him so subdued. "She's all right, Pete. She..."

"What's going on! One minute she was fine, the next she was driving away. I don't understand."

"It's a long story. Liz knows the ins and outs. We'll get Cath settled then Liz will be over to see you."

"Can I come to yours? I could..."

"No, mate. It's best you wait for Liz. I only know half a tale so wait for her."

By the time Liz arrived I was climbing the walls. Her first five minutes was spent putting brandy inside me and calming me down.

"I don't know how much Liz has told you of her past," she began.

"Everything," I interrupted. "We've told each other everything."

"She was married young."

"Yes, when she was seventeen. Her family disowned her."

"And there was... there was..."

"A baby. Yes. She told me. He died and the husband left her."

"It was a bad time for her. Stuck in a pokey flat in a town she didn't know, no-one to turn to."

"I know all this!" I took a deep breath. "Sorry, Liz, but I know all this."

"So you know how she got through it."

"Yes, music. All she did for weeks was listen to music until, she said, the hurt had gone away."

"And do you know what music in particular?"

I groaned. Liz squeezed my hand.

"That night you went to see Johnny's band at The Grapes and we stayed behind, she told me all about it. Bob Marley saved her, she said, but now she can't bear to listen to him. He means survival and hope, but he also means loss."

Did he mean loss for me too, I wondered.

*

Cath returned in the morning, ashamed and apologetic. We talked for hours but the distance that had opened up between us didn't close. I knew I'd have to do something special.

A week later, Johnny's band had another gig. Cath was bullied by Liz into joining us there where she stood listless and disengaged until, halfway through a rowdy first set, Johnny quietened the crowd down.

"Right, you lot. We've a special treat for you tonight. For one night only, and one song only, thank God, let me introduce you to Mr Peter Atkinson!"

The baffled crowd didn't exactly go wild as I shuffled on to the stage, apart from a few guffawing friends who knew I couldn't carry a tune in a bucket, but I didn't see them. The only person I saw was Cath, her preoccupation blown away by confusion that turned to tears when she heard the first notes of the tune Johnny picked out on his guitar.

Redemption Song was written by Bob Marley near the end of his career when he already knew he had cancer. Some people reckon it's his greatest song – one acoustic guitar, one voice, and lyrics filled with pain and mortality. I'd never sung in front of an audience, except in nightmares, but I did my best: a tremulous voice falling into a crowd grown silent because, although they didn't understand what, they knew they were witnessing something profound. I gazed at Cath through the spotlights, her tears still flowing but her smile restored, and I managed to get halfway through the second verse before my throat became too tight to go on and Johnny had to finish the song alone because I was off the stage, surrounded by a mass of cheering people, my arms around her, neither of us able to speak, our embrace saying everything.

*

Next week is our tenth wedding anniversary. Cath doesn't know it yet, but we'll spend it in Jamaica. While we're there, I'll take her to see the home of her hero. And mine.

The Magician

Lynn Valentine

Knit me some light
to bookend each day,
shortening Winter-long;
White wool in plain-stitch
to brighten the hours.
A heart spinning heat
to line time with gold;
I turn as you conjure
possibility of sun.

STOC

Julie Christie

The rigs, newly ploughèd
Ran in straight lines, rigid,
As if into the Firth drownèd.

Seumas with the sunlight hair,
Freckles and aquarius eyes starèd
At Seanmhair's brow, furrows etchèd
He knew not the reasons for
Apart from to him she was old
Hard-working crofting hands
To touch, were cold.

As his scarf she tièd
Around his neck, so tight,
He dancèd on the spot
Like a marionette.
Well, this is how to me he appearèd,
His worn catalogue shoes polishèd
Like a Highland soldier's marching boots.

The knot finally fastenèd
The Stoc fell to show
Gorm, glas, doinne blendèd
After plants and herbs collectèd
In plain stitch knittèd
In horizontal lines
By hands cripplèd
During the Winter freeze.

The boy shot off
Like bullets that killèd
Deer while in heather grazèd
Only to stop dead
To clamber over the gate

Of wooden geometric design
By Seanair, many Summers ago, craftèd.

Track taking Seumas onwards
Maybe even upwards
To where the buzzard hoverèd
Before to pause on the fence post
To better aim at his prey.

Further, further,
Past the erect Scots Pines
To the Clootie Well
Make a spell?
Talk to the Sithean?
Look deeper down?
Look into the Future?
The water clear
Cool to touch
Words in the Salm at church
Imagination magnifièd.

"Seumas: What did you learn at the school today?"
At Seanmhair's wrinkles he lookèd,
Like the ticking clock around he turnèd
Trappèin the Stoc, he slippèd away.

The Gaelic language was spoken on Eilean Dubh (Black Isle) and surrounding Highland & Island areas before it was systematically eradicated in many places by legislation and changes in population and culture.

The Gaelic Language (Scotland) Act 2005 received Royal Assent on the 1st June 2005. Enshrined in the Act is the aspiration that Gaelic should enjoy equal respect with the English language in Scotland.

This is my attempt to introduce you to some Gàidhlig words with a poem written in the style of a Salm (a Psalm) - part of the Gàidhlig heritage.

Translation:
Stoc = scarf
Seumas = James
Seanair = Grandfather
Seanmhair = Grandmother
gorm = blue
glas = grey
doinne =brown
Sithean = fairies, also means Peace.

Indian Summer

Elizabeth Waters

Every stone can feel my rapture,
Every twig and blade of grass;
Every lingering breath of summer
Feels my spirit as I pass.
High above the berried branches
In the deepening blue,
The birds are waiting for the winter
And I am waiting too.
But I see only ripening redness
Of autumn fruit along the bough,
And pay no heed to threats of winter
So long as it seems summer now.
For if I can hold this stolen moment,
When winter 's almost in the fields,
Then I can drink the mellow hope
This Indian Summer yields.
And I can keep it through the winter,
Through the months of darkening cold.
So I will drink of warm October
As deeply as my heart can hold.

The Deadly Snow

Jeremy Price

He'd experienced cold winters before, but never anything as severe as this. He recalled his grandfather's expression about the 'perishing cold' and now it had real meaning. His own cocoon of sleeping bag and blankets afforded little protection from the icy envelope that had sealed his world for the last six weeks.

The change in weather had been comparatively sudden. The sky, usually crisp and blue during the shorter days, became a dull, featureless grey and it stayed that way as the temperature plummeted to levels he'd never before known. The sparse greenery outside had long since given up its search for sunlight and died, gasping for the wherewithal to survive.

He, unlike the plants, was conversant with survival in hostile environments having spent years working the more remote field stations, often in outrageously secluded situations. But he loved the bleakness; he could indulge his passion for solitude, reading and writing voraciously. He had little need for human companionship, preferring instead the isolation that his job provided. Contact with his employers was kept to an absolute minimum and the readings that the bank of elaborate technological equipment harvested and digested were then burped into the ether to be caught in an electronic net somewhere and interpreted.

Six weeks ago the activities and messaging ceased abruptly. The computers crashed without even the courtesy of a warning and the communications facilities shut down. The generator, which was the heart of his community of one, continued its operation of pumping power as if it was lifeblood, to provide light and heat for the computers and complex itself. But like a comatose body the vital functions idled and the mental capacities ceased. He could no longer communicate with the outside world, even if he wanted to.

He'd been alarmed at first, working to re-establish networks, but after a few short hours the realisation had sunk in that his predicament was dire. Logic and instinct kept him focused on survival; he assumed help would come when the lack of communications made it obvious all was not well.

But help did not come and the weather worsened. There was something different about this, though. A continuous, unchanging and claustrophobic blanket of grey shrouded the breathtaking chill. Light, if it could be called light, was as it would be in dense fog – bedimmed, adumbrated. As the snow fell, so did his spirit with the certainty that liberation was a futile hope.

The signs had all been there when he last heard the news. A worsening Middle Eastern crisis, the escalation in global tension. Unlike his surroundings, the situation became all too clear. Massive electro-magnetic pulses from the bombs had wiped out all digital communications as surely as they had wiped out entire cities, whole populations. The dust from the enormous explosions, almost certainly radioactive, had been thrown high into the atmosphere and was now descending with the snow, sullying its beauty and choking the world's ecosystems which foundered in the grip of a nuclear winter.

Anguish

Judy Harvey

Darkness looms as night draws near.
Moonlight shines through dark clouds.
Wind howls through the swaying trees.
Lightning flashes as thunder cracks.
The Devil waits to savage him.

He knows the night terrors well.
The many hours of agony.
Enduring pain – Grasping on to sanity.
Determined to survive and heal.
God's blessings to sustain him.

Hard rain plummets the windows.
Echoes of the sound vibrate in his head.
His brain, his thoughts take him elsewhere.
The torment begins – he prepares for war.
The Devil has attacked.

His muscles tighten like a coiled spring.
His skin turns red as a hot coal fire.
He is drenched in cold sweat.
Waves of intractable pain flood his body.
The Devil's cruel grip tightens.

Nausea swirls in his queasy stomach.
His feet and legs swell and ache.
It is impossible to stand - they give way.
He falls – crawling into the bathroom vomiting.
The Devil will not relent.

He pulls himself into bed.
The pillows cradle his throbbing head.
His brain is screaming – his heart is pounding.
His breathing is laboured – he must be still.
The Devil persists.

The love he so desperately needs eludes him.
Hypersensitivity produces excruciating sensations
preventing tender human touch.
He lies there stoically in prayer – crying out to God for mercy.
His faith steadfast.

Exhausted and broken – he eventually passes out.
Battle weary but alive – he sleeps – at last.
The sunlight of a bright dawn gently awakens him.
He smiles courageously with renewed hope – God's grace has won!
Perhaps the Devil won't attack him tonight.

I have a dog whose name is Sandie

Dorrie Robertson

I have a dog whose name is Sandie.
His legs are short
and rather bandy.
"But I don't mind,"
said little dog Sandie,
"I'm attached to my legs
and they come in handy."

The Cinnamon Doughnut

Evelyn Topp

Once there was a little granny who lived in a house up the Hill of Fortrose. She was a very modern granny and wouldn't have liked to be called 'a little old woman' as in most fairy tales. She was very involved in the WRI and was constantly baking and making things for competitions and shows. She also loved watching television cookery programmes, and her favourite by far was 'The Great British Bake Off' with Mary Berry and Paul Hollywood. One evening the contestants were given the challenge of baking with yeast and had to make doughnuts. "Goodness, it's been years since I made doughnuts," thought Granny, "that would be a fine treat for Maya and Ruairidh when they come home from school tomorrow."

So the next morning she made up some dough, and once it had risen, she fetched out her deep fat fryer (as she was a modern granny she had all these labour-saving devices) and set to work. The doughnuts cooked to perfection, crisp and golden, and she tossed them in cinnamon sugar. They smelled delicious! "Heavens, is that the time?" she said to herself, "I'll just try one for my elevenses." She bit into one of the doughnuts. "Mmmmm, wonderful," she said licking the sugar off her fingers, "the children will love these. I might just have another." But one doughnut who had watched his brother being eaten, leapt down off the plate and rolled out the door. "Hey", yelled Granny, "come back!" But the Cinnamon Doughnut rolled on.

"Roll, roll, roll away,

"You won't eat me! No way, Jose!" he shouted.

Granny ran after him but he wouldn't stop.

Before long, he met some tourists who had been climbing up Swallow Den.

"What a great view," said one, "but I could do with a bite to eat."

"Well I never!" said his friend, "was that a doughnut that just rolled by? Quick, grab it!"

But the Cinnamon Doughnut wouldn't stop. He shouted,

"Roll, roll, roll away.

"You won't eat me! No way, Jose!"

And on he rolled, pursued by the two tourists and Granny.

He rolled down The Wards past the church and swung left towards Rosemarkie. At the Police Station he turned sharp right and headed down Ness Road, forcing an oncoming car to make an emergency stop. Two policemen who were in the car park were alerted by the screech of brakes. "Did you see that?" said one, "over the speed limit and no signal. We'll nab him for speeding AND dangerous driving." And they ran to their patrol car.

But the Cinnamon Doughnut wouldn't stop. He shouted,

"Roll, roll, roll away,

"You won't eat me! No way, Jose!"

And on he rolled, pursued by the police car with blue flashing lights and siren blaring, the two tourists and Granny.

"Oh dear," thought the Cinnamon Doughnut, "this police car is going to catch me." Just then he spied the path leading from Ness Road where, of course, the police car couldn't follow him. He gave a sigh of relief as he came out on to Greengates Place, right in front of a class of Fortrose Academy pupils who were out on a cross-country run. Now several of these children were quite chubby and were puffing along at barely a jog, listening to their ipods. Their teacher was encouraging them to keep up when they spotted the Cinnamon Doughnut.

"Hey, guys, a doughnut!" shouted one, "just the sort of unhealthy snack we all love. Let's catch him!" and they sped up, passing the teacher who yelled after them, "Not so fast! Pace your-selves!" but they paid him no attention.

"Roll, roll, roll away.

"You won't eat me! No way, Jose!" shouted the Cinnamon Doughnut.

He ran through the caravan site pursued by the school pupils, the tourists and Granny. He could hear the police car coming so he ran on to the Golf Course.

A foursome of players were on the course as the Cinnamon Doughnut rolled by. "Fore!" they yelled but the Cinnamon

Doughnut took no notice, narrowly avoiding being hit by a golf ball.

"Roll, roll, roll away.

"You won't eat me! No way, Jose!" he shouted defiantly.

On he went, pursued by the golfers, the school pupils, the tourists and Granny while the police car kept pace with them down Ness Road towards Chanonry Point.

As usual, there was a crowd of people gathered at the lighthouse watching the dolphins tumbling and leaping offshore. As the Cinnamon Doughnut and his pursuers arrived they turned in amazement and rushed over to see what was happening. The Cinnamon Doughnut jinked round the police car and found to his horror that he had run out of road. Behind him was a crowd of people anxious to get their hands and teeth on him. He stood on the jetty and looked across the water at Ardersier and Fort George. If only he could get across. Suddenly a sleek grey shape surfaced in the sea beside him. "I can help you," said the dolphin holding up his bottlenose, "jump on." The Cinnamon Doughnut leapt on to the dolphin's snout and the dolphin tossed him into the air, just as he would a salmon, and chomped him in two. Sadly that was the end of the Cinnamon Doughnut.

"Yum," said the dolphin smiling a happy smile, "I think I like cinnamon doughnuts!"

Knockando

Jo Mulkerrin

By the moor of Ballintomb
Through woodland, hill and moor
The old Strathspey railway stretched
From Boat to Aberlour.

Bridges crossed the burns and bog,
The trains went steaming through;
At Blacksboat station they would stop
Near the mill at Knockando.

It was here the farmer's fleeces
Were converted into yarn,
Woven on the Dobcross loom and
Stacked in the station barn.

Collecting cargos of rough blankets
The train carried them to town,
To clothe the men who went to war:
The red, the green, the brown.

The flood that came in '45
Ripped through the weaving shed;
The wool, the yarn, even the loom
Dragged down to the burn bed.

Undaunted, Duncan Stewart fought
To save his precious living,
To keep alive Knockando's pride
He was driven.

'Grade A' and 'sole survivor'
Are the epithets now used;
New born from old,
Warmth out of cold,
Life not refused.

The Seven Sisters of Kintail

An old tale retold

Elizabeth Sutherland

In the time before the time that was, a crofter fisherman lived by Loch Duich who had seven daughters, each as beautiful as the dawn. One stormy night a great ship was driven on to the shore, and with it, two handsome, golden-haired Viking brothers. While their father helped the crew to refurbish the ship, the seven maidens all fell in love with the two Norse lords.

When the ship was mended, the brothers asked the crofter for the hands of his two youngest daughters. When the older maidens heard of this they were indignant.

"It's not fair," said one, "I am the oldest. I should be married first."

"And I am the second oldest," echoed another, "therefore I should be married next."

"I am the most beautiful," said the third daughter, "so I should have been chosen."

"But I am the best cook," grumbled the fourth, "so why wasn't I chosen?"

"And I am the cleverest of us all," said the fifth (which, by the way, wasn't exactly true).

"It's not fair," they all chorused as they wiped away their tears.

The two brothers listened to them and nodded their heads. "All you say is true," they agreed. "But," said one of them, "we have five brothers, all of them older, all of them richer and all of them wiser than we are."

The five maidens lifted their heads and began to listen.

"Surely the older sisters should go to the older brothers," said the other lordling.

"When we tell them about you, they will certainly all fall in love with you."

The girls dried their eyes. "Will you take us with you?" the oldest sister begged.

"Better than that," said the first lord. "Within a year and a day we will bring them here to you. What a wedding that will be!"

"Will you really do that for us?" said the clever one who was not clever at all.

"We will, we will," said the brothers earnestly.

So the two young brides sailed away with their two young lords and as far as we know they lived happily ever after.

Meanwhile the five older sisters prepared happily for their joint wedding to the five richer, more handsome brothers who were coming all the way from Norroway. Every morning one of them rose early to watch the horizon for a sign of their ship.

They waited and they waited. Meanwhile other suitors came from far and wide to woo them but all were rejected. "We are waiting for our lovers from Norroway," they replied. "They will be here any day now."

The weeks turned into months and the months into a year but still the brothers did not come.

Now there lived in those parts a wise man who was known as the Grey Magician of Coire Dhuinnid. After a year and a day he paid the sisters a visit.

"Why do you wait for these faithless lords?" he asked.

"They will come," the maidens assured him. "You'll see."

Every year the Grey Magician visited the croft. Every year he asked the same question. Every year the maidens grew older and sadder but not, alas, wiser for every year they told him the same story. "We are still waiting."

One year when they were old the Grey Magician took pity on them. "Wait for them forever, then," he told them and turned them into mountains.

So the Five Sisters of Kintail still wait and watch for the ship that never comes.

A cautionary tale about Leonard, who ignored his mother's wishes and went out guising on Hallowe'en...

Jeremy Price

Leonard was the type of boy
Who childish pranks did oft employ.
He'd target family and friends
But never sought to make amends.

April Fool's Day planning started
Just as Christmas had departed.
His repertoire of jokes extended
All year round, and he intended
Making mischief all his life
Regardless of collateral strife.

His mother told him
"Leonard – stop!
Or I shall really blow my top.
You really think you're having fun
But mind out – you will hurt someone."

One dark October night his mate
Said "Leonard – wouldn't it be great
If we did something quite surprising?
Let's dress up and go out guising."

Once again his mother frowned
"Actions such as this compound
Your reputation, now in tatters.
Safety, too, that really matters.
You shouldn't mess with unseen forces;
No human understands the sources
Of the evil you will meet
If you play games like *Trick or Treat*."

Against her will the hapless lad
(quite convinced his mum was mad)
Found costume, make-up, books of magic.
Ignoring consequences tragic
Set out to spook and thrill and scream
That fateful, horrid Hallowe'en.

So, dressed in black young Leonard went
To have his fill of this event,
But so excited, flushed and ruddy
Forgot to call on his best buddy
And headed to the edge of toon
To the bridge across the River Doon.

Now, you and I know Tam O'Shanter
And Maggie – hardly at a canter –
Lost her tail to hellish legions
(not the sort you call Glaswegians)
As they crossed the running water
To avoid the witches' slaughter.

But now our Leonard, dressed so ghoulish,
Wished he'd never been so foolish
To ignore his mother's wishes
As he heard the ghostly swishes
Of the witches in the night
And the ghoulies giving fright.

But dressing like a scary monster
Ended with complete disaster.
Out they came to greet a friend,
A ghostly horde on him descend
And swept him up, their arms unfurled
To drag him to the underworld.
Beware, all ye who would go guising:
Take ma heed as one despising
Playing wi' the darker forces
Is not what anyone endorses.

Leonard's gone – his tricks nae mare.
His mother often says a prayer
In hope that soon he will return
From disappearing by that burn
Where forces totally unseen
Do ride abroad on Hallowe'en.

I Remember

Russell Turner

I remember a summer day, a bend in the road
I remember gravel, broken metal, broken bone
I remember silence
I remember concerned faces, helping hands, a helicopter
I survived – so did my motorbike

Harker's Escape

Jenny Fyfe

It was better not to argue with Margaret, Harker decided after only a few weeks of marriage. During their short engagement, entered into three months after they met, he had not noticed that Margaret was an aggressive woman who could not bear to be in the wrong. Perhaps she had deliberately acted in an untypically conciliatory manner in order not to lose him, or he had been so much in love with this undoubtedly attractive lady that he saw nothing beyond her skin-deep beauty.

It did not take long for things to change after marriage. He was not normally a stupid man, but he realized very quickly that he had been foolish to jump into matrimony with someone who expected to have her own way in everything, whether it was a big decision like which house to buy or a small one like whether he should continue with his pre-marriage preference to eat pudding with a dessertspoon. According to Margaret, it should be eaten with a fork or, if slippery like blancmange, with a fork and spoon together but, never, ever, with a single spoon.

Even though he trained himself to keep silent when she attacked him, everything about Margaret irritated him and he longed to wind time back to his earlier wife-free days. Then, during one of her verbal assaults, he suddenly realized that much of what she said was really quite amusing. Instead of withdrawing his attention from her words, he should pay more attention. He should write about her rantings and turn them into humorous fiction.

But how could he write about her, or anything else for that matter, unless he had a space of his own where he could work without her disturbing him every two minutes? She did not know that writing was something that, except in special circumstances, had to be done in uninterrupted peace. Harker was not like Jane Austen, who could work at a parlour table while the rest of the family continued their lives around her. There was nowhere in the house where Margaret would not be the dominant person present, talking, arguing, ordering this or that to be done.

Margaret, however, suffered from acrophobia to the extent that she could not climb the ladder into the loft. She tried once, when they first moved in, but could not do it. Harker could therefore have free run of the attic. Bit by bit he moved small items of furniture into what he envisioned as a true writer's study. He acquired a chair that Margaret had decided was ready for the skip, and a card table lying disused at the back of a cupboard. Card tables, Margaret decreed, were for playing cards on, an occupation engaged in only by people with too much time on their hands and nothing sensible to fill it with.

So the card table became Harker's writing desk in his upstairs study. He bought a few extra items like a reading lamp, a laptop, printer, and the necessary stationery. He was a writer now, not just Margaret's husband. To tell the truth, Margaret was quite pleased to have him out of the way for a few hours a day.

At any rate, she let him have his privacy in the attic even although when he was downstairs she thought it was her duty to watch over him, talk to him constantly, and make sure that he did not transgress any of her rules of etiquette. Now that he had learned to listen to her so attentively, she thought that her good training had begun to take effect. It did not occur to her that he had any ulterior motive for paying her such close heed. She thought her marriage had been a success and was glad for it. Margaret was not a bad woman, merely an irritating one.

So Harker escaped into his writing and his loved attic room. He continued to cultivate his amusement about Margaret's foibles. He listened carefully and took note of all her funny ways so that he could write about them in a style that would appeal to aficionados of the best humorous fiction.

One day, however, when it was cold in the attic, Margaret had gone out shopping, leaving an open wood fire blazing in the living room (with a guard of course, Margaret would never risk leaving a fire unattended without a guard). Harker decided it would be safe to come down and work beside the fire for a little while. He brought with him a writing pad to draft the next chapter of his novel and the notebook in which he was accustomed to enter stray ideas that occurred to him, along with pieces of useful dialogue.

He meant to go upstairs again, taking his work with him, before Margaret returned. Suddenly, however, he heard her key turn in the lock and immediately raced upstairs, forgetting the notebook in his haste, forgetting also that Margaret was inordinately curious and believed that she had the right to read anything in the house. At the beginning he had tried to dissuade her from opening his personal correspondence, but she just went on reading it, saying, "I'm your wife, you know. Of course I can read your letters whenever I want". Now she believed she had not only the right but the duty to find out what Harker's notebook contained.

Harker, settling again to his work in the attic, looked for the notebook. It was not there, so he went downstairs to fetch it.

He found Margaret incandescent with rage. She had thrown the notebook in the fire as soon as she had realized the notes were about her and were far from complimentary. There was to be no more writing in the attic. Harker's only mode of escape now was through the divorce courts. No-one will ever know if he could have been the famous satirical writer that he had thought he might become, or whether he was just the petty, selfish, inconsiderate, duplicitous husband that Margaret spent the rest of her life warning other women against.

Ode to Life

Jack Hermiston

As each day dawned I died a little more
Before the labour of my day began.
My life and work which once I'd held in awe
Induced the thought to flee.
I lived my time in sisyphean toil
In unremitting ennui.

When they that matter say that time is money
Where goes my need for air and space and beauty.
Lack promotes the lessening of my being
And leaves me full of spleen.
Sustenance from these things dear to me
Lay buried and unseen.

I turned to a seductive, ancient aid
Which spoke of fire and peat and ripening barley.
Glistening, glowing with an aureate sheen,
It loosed a sense of freedom.
Aqua Vitae gave me back my life
And made me fly from tedium.

It is life's task to gladden all my senses:
Flowers whose scent can raise a poet's ardour;
A setting sun with islands bathed in red;
To these I'm now related.
A poem declaimed with feeling and with grace
Is splendid and exalted.

When riding waves my life went elemental
And I sailed to use the power that's free,
I joined the birds and fish to swoop and turn
And be no longer chained.
I watched the tide and marvelled at its power
And knew my soul had gained.

When seeking treasures on the land and sea:
A single daffodil is worth a ransom;
The surge and swish when cleaving through the water
Sets exaltation alight.
The beauty of the earth is now my playground
For I have taken flight.

Closing the Generation Gap
Judy Harvey

He didn't feel his age and didn't accept any limitations. He was eager to tackle his everyday routine even though it took him several hours to complete. Today he rose early so he would be ready for this special day. He dressed in his usual shirt, jumper and trousers and slipped into his favourite blue anorak. It took him a hour to walk to the beach and that was with many pauses.

The breeze off the sea blew in his face and rumpled his curly grey hair. He steadied himself as he walked along the hard-packed sand. He was much bent over now and his walk was slow and unsteady, but determined. His deep blue eyes had lost some of their lustre and he strained to see the image coming towards him. However, when he smiled, his eyes twinkled with joy at the sight of her.

She walked unsteadily and awkwardly. The sea breeze blew her soft blonde curls and the sea mist made her giggle with delight. She had sparkling blue eyes and a button nose with a toothless smile. She stumbled once or twice and got sand on her hands but she righted herself almost instantly. She was determined to continue her walk to the familiar man who was walking towards her. She jumped with glee as he put out his arms to her. As he scooped her up, his back creaked, but he paid no mind.

"Oh Great Grandpa," she exclaimed, as she gave him a big gooey kiss.

"Oh Amelia," he said hugging her tightly with tears of happiness in his eyes.

No Way to Redemption

Eleanore Simpson

What with house-hunting and my first pregnancy I had been too self-absorbed to give my young cousin more than a passing thought for ages. It was the mid seventies and the housing market in Edinburgh was really hotting up. I was surprised when she phoned.

"That was Chrissie," I told my husband. "She wants to have a chat with me tomorrow about something. I invited her to join us for lunch with the others, but she said she wasn't too good in the mornings; could she come after lunch instead. Perhaps she's pregnant!" We both laughed.

Chrissie arrived looking her usual elegant self, managing to appear chic wearing blue stonewashed jeans and a baggy green polo-necked sweater – certainly not the conventional image of a second-year art student who was into painting abstracts. But her body language whispered of distress and tension.

She asked for a glass of milk and joined in the small talk over coffee, her social training kicking her into autopilot. Our baby started to cry and everyone went "Aw...". That was my cue to say, "Feeding time by the sound of it. Chrissie, come on through and keep me company... Please excuse us everyone."

I picked up my wailing three-month-old daughter and offered her to Chrissie to hold while I organised a fresh nappy. She backed off rapidly. "I don't know anything about babies," she said. So I did my usual coping-with-one-hand routine while trying to soothe the little one.

Once tiny tot was all fresh again, I sat on the easy chair and plugged her in so to speak. I looked up at Chrissie, willing her to say something. She picked up the cue, but turned away to stare out of the window at the budding daffodils in the window box. Her shoulders slumped and her head bent forwards. Then she got a grip, swept her cascade of auburn hair away from her face, stood up straight and said quietly, "I'm pregnant." She was still, apparently contemplating those burgeoning daffodils.

"Oh!" was all I could think of to say, but I was thinking plenty.

"Are you sure? How far gone do you think you are? We could work it out."

"I'm sure. The doctor confirmed it. I'm eight weeks now. I don't know what to do."

"Who's the father? Do you want to get married to him?"

"It's David. You know. I've known him since primary school. But since his motor bike accident he hasn't been quite right in the head. My parents don't approve of my being with him any more. I feel sorry for him, but I don't want to marry him. I haven't told him about the baby and don't plan to, either."

"So where does this leave you?"

"Well, I hate to think of an abortion but if I have one I'm nearly at the deadline already. If I have the baby I couldn't give it up for adoption. I just couldn't. I couldn't go through the pregnancy and birth and not want to keep it. But if I kept it, I could never go home again. Dad wouldn't be able to hold his head up in the town. Everyone would talk and he wouldn't be able to stand that. He'd blame Mum and then that would be the end of their marriage. I couldn't do that to her."

"Have you talked to your mum?"

"No, I'm planning to go tomorrow. I'll tell Dad it's a spur of the moment surprise visit and I'll get Mum on her own after lunch. I need to talk to her. I couldn't bear to keep this a secret from her."

"Good idea. I've got lots of books on pregnancy and babies. Take them to read on the bus. You might want to clue up on stuff before you make your final decision."

*

My aunt dug the fork into the damp earth to loosen a stubborn weed before she howked it out and flung it into the rubbish bucket along with the other rejects.

"My mother used to say she'd buried many a sorrow in the garden. Her three eldest children were killed in the First World War. I never knew my brothers. And now, right about now, I am losing my first...". Her voice broke into silence.

"That Sunday two weeks ago I was coming back from church

and I saw this waif dragging herself up the road. I hardly recognised her. The first thing she said was, "Oh Mum, I had to come to see you. I'm pregnant." I was flummoxed. I told her to go home and chat to her dad while I got some cream from the corner shop, and we would talk later, just us two. I had to buy myself some time. I couldn't think what to say to her. Why oh why did she have to go and do that thing?"

*

Dandling my six-month-old son affectionately on his knee, my uncle looked round at the guests at his silver wedding party lunch and beamed at me and his wife. "Isn't this all grand, and what a fine little fellow you have here. I can't wait for Chrissie to have one of her own."

He never did discover what sacrifices had been made for him.

It's my family made me this way

Dorrie Robertson

I know I seem odd,
But honest to god
It's my family made me this way.

Dad wasn't bad,
But mother went mad
And did things strange and mysterious.
They took her away
One dark winter's day
When she got quite deranged and delirious.

My husband Dan was a violent man,
He killed a boy in a fight.
They put him away for a very long time
I think they did perfectly right.

My daughter Denise has joined the police
But I don't think she'll get to the top.
She spends her weekends
Doing drugs with her friends,
That isn't right for a cop.

I know I seem odd,
But honest to god
It's my family made me this way.

The Red Kite

Lynn Valentine

We laid a hedge in November, planting the bare roots at the boundary of the field in the hope that these spindly twigs would protect us from winters to come. We worked silently, side by side, digging and smoothing the black earth.

Your pink boots marked you out as a city girl, new to this place of green Barbour jackets and muddy wellies. I kept casting you sly glances as you dug, amazed that your manicured hands could turn this practical.

You looked up from your work, "There he is again Niall!" you shouted.

The Red Kite wheeled overhead, hunting prey or perhaps hopeful of a morsel being turned from the soil by our weary arms. We watched him hovering above us, before he veered off in the direction of the Firth.

We smiled across at each other. The Red Kite was a good omen, affirmation that we had made the right choice in moving. He would stay here year-round, you said – you'd read that somewhere. He didn't need to migrate to warmer climes. We worked on, spirits lifted, making the task at hand easier.

The hedge would replace the trees we had cut in the summer. We craved a view of the mountains more than we wanted shelter from the breeze.

So down the conifers came, a day's work for the local contractors, the two of them making you blush with their banter throughout the day. They had been gone a week when the real weather roared through.

So the hedge was planned and paid for, a hundred white wild rose bushes that would bring the bees and filter the wind.

We made a good job of it, you and I.

By the time spring came the roses were beginning to bud, leaves greening on the slender sticks. I stood alone in the garden watching the Red Kite with his mate crying alongside him, both on the hunt for sustenance.

A cautionary tale about Tim, whose delight in cheese ended in disaster

Jeremy Price
(with apologies to Hilaire Belloc)

Tim from the Antipodes
Devoted half his life to cheese.
In search of even more to please
He travelled near and overseas.
As time went by he yearned for stronger,
Forays growing even longer.

One day he found himself, by chance,
In a fromagerie in France.
In front of him a vast expanse
Of cheese put him in a trance.
Just the strong – not average –
Tim bought and stored them in his fridge.

For many weeks the stockpile grew
As Tim did many sorts accrue.
Each one was savoured with a chew,
But all the while the residue
Created gases which increased
The pressure, needing swift release.

Finally, one fateful day
The fridge door blasted clean away.
The build-up of the cheesy fume
Sent noxious gases in a plume,
And liquid cheese, a living spume
Killed everybody in the room.

The moral, please let me suggest,
With foodstuffs don't become obsessed.
Tim's friends and family will attest,
The spouses will be unimpressed
If you feel need to pay homage
To butter, yoghurt or fromage.

Time Not Taken

Pam Macintyre

So much to do,
Mustn't be late for work,
Children to feed,
Be on time for school,
Swimming lessons,
Dancing lessons,
Gymnastics too.
And the rest.

"Here's your lunch, Mum."
(Baked potato with butter, cold meat and salad).
"Will you be ok till teatime? Must dash."

And you sat in your chair looking out over the garden you could
no longer tend.
Sometimes you read, or watched the news on television,
listened to a play on the radio, or sat thinking and remembering.
One day after lunch you went to a different chair by the window.
You said, "I'll be all right soon, let me sit here for a while."
And later you said, "My mind went. I couldn't remember
anything, but now I can."
Your hands could barely hold a knife and fork, and you only
wore clothes you could dress yourself in, and those kitchen taps:
"Don't turn them off too tightly, remember?"
Shuffling feet in slippers that were once brisk steps in neat shoes
on the lino floor still took you about the house, just at a slower
pace.

Then you were ill in bed and the Christmas tree was brought
through to your bedroom for you to enjoy. You loved Christmas
time. Is that why you chose to leave us then?
You were only in hospital for a week before you slipped away
early on Christmas Day when children were opening their
stockings and turkey for ten was being prepared.

And time had run out.

Then with the grief came the guilt.
Car trips that should have been taken, but were not.
Time taken for listening and talking, that was not.
More patience shown and kindness given, but was not.

Years later an old lady said of one of her grown-up sons who
lived with her,
"He never tells me anything. I never know when he'll be in for
tea, or even at home."
His silence caused much pain and frustration and she had lost
confidence.
Her husband had died not long before and home had become a
place of little hope.

If this was a second chance I cannot say, but I knew I wanted to
do something to help.

So now we enjoy outings in the car, stopping wherever the fancy
takes.
Memories are relived, and family gossip aired over coffee and
cake.
Unsure whether she should bother someone about her painful
hips, it was easy to listen and encourage her as she thought
through the problem out loud, and then take her to the doctor, to
hospital appointments, and to visit her at home after her
operations. Her world has opened up. She attends her various
afternoon clubs once more, and looks forward to seeing the rest
of her family at weekends when not busy with their own lives.

I can give to her what I did not give to my own mother.
Time. So elusive to find, so easy to fritter, but ours to make.

The Time is Now

Claire Hemsworth

Enjoy the moment,
Seize the day,
Take each opportunity
That comes your way.

The time is now,
Don't let it go.
It will soon pass you by
If you say 'no'.

For special moments
Pause and time spend;
You can't bring them back
At the day's end.

Children's achievements,
Lover's call;
Whispers from heaven,
Make time for them all.

These times can't be forced,
They quickly appear;
And if you're not careful,
They soon disappear.

Special moments to treasure,
With those we hold dear.
If we rest and we listen,
Even God will draw near.

He'll whisper "I love you,
I'll look after you."
And if you just let him,
Your hope he'll renew.

These moments we'll miss,
No treasures we'll find –
If we don't pause our lives
'Cause we didn't have time.

Looking (1)

Sheena Munro

"Don't keep looking at your feet," said the physio,
"have confidence in yourself, hold your head up high."
But my feet stayed shackled to the ground, unwilling to believe
they could learn to walk again.
So I shuffled along, longing once more to see
the wispy wind-driven clouds, and the greening branches;
to hear the eager birds exchanging their greetings
and to feel the encouraging breeze.
And then I saw it, a splash of damascene glory
on the grey of the concrete, spreading its silken wings
Imperial purple on the chilly pavement,
a Peacock butterfly; and I gave a prayer of thanks
for the sad lame legs that had saved me from crushing that glory
and the eyes unwilling to rise from the grey of the street.

Looking (2)

"Mind where you put your feet – it's slippery there."
A dark winter evening – not the wisest of times
to be walking that quiet road, with the air so keen.
But – "doesn't Orion look wonderful tonight?"
and the previous warning went unheeded now
as we gazed up wondering into the network of frost-fire.
And there it was, silently shimmering, shivering
across the worshipping darkness – the Aurora.
Our souls thrilled, and we felt time hold its breath
as I heard myself murmur : "The heavens
declare the glory of God."

Time

Russell Turner

When the clock stopped at midnight, Wilson knew he was going to die.

He'd sat for most of the evening in a candlelit silence dominated by the clock's insistent tick-tock, watching the brass pendulum swing, remembering. At one minute before midnight he'd poured more whisky and waited for the second hand to reach twelve, the clock's chimes heralded by a series of clicks and whirrs muffled by its tarnished walnut casing. But the pendulum stopped, the chimes were stillborn, and Wilson knew he was going to die.

Rebecca had found the clock. They'd been in town seeking more practical items to furnish their new home when she wandered through the open door of an antique shop. "We must have it!" she'd exclaimed. "How can we live in an old farmhouse without a grandfather clock? It will look wonderful in the corner of the living room." Wilson could deny her nothing. For three years he'd spoiled her and loved her and been happy to do so. Only three years.

A log shifted in the fireplace, generating a brief burst of heat soon lost in a room chilled by freezing fog that penetrated every chink in the two-hundred-year-old building. The power had failed hours ago. Wilson shivered, crossed to the windows and pulled the heavy curtains more tightly across them, then returned to his armchair and downed the whisky. He slopped more into his glass, careless of drops that spattered the dust-covered table top.

Maybe a minute, maybe an hour had passed when Wilson became conscious of soft movement behind the curtains. He stood, uncertain for a moment, gulped more whisky and strode across the room where he flung back the rose-patterned brocade that Rebecca had loved. Written in the condensation on the glass was a single, dripping, word: "TIME".

Wilson hadn't meant to kill Rebecca. How could he harm someone who meant so much? But when she told him there was someone else, someone less... intense, he remembered nothing, heard nothing, until the clock struck twelve and he found her body at his feet.

Three heavy thumps on the farmhouse door jolted Wilson back to the present. He lifted the candle and crept from living room to kitchen, each step slower than the one before, until he faced the door, oak illuminated by quavering flame.

"Who's there?"

The reply was silence, shattered by three more thumps.

Wilson seized the iron handle and wrenched the door open. Freezing air poured in. The light was snuffed out. In the shadows he could see no-one.

"Rebecca!" he yelled. "Rebecca, please!" No answer.

Around him, the fog danced and shifted to reveal the frost-shrouded apple tree they'd planted in their first year at the farm-house. Wilson took a long shaky breath and stumbled into the garden, toward the mound beneath the tree. There, he lay down beside her, stared up, far beyond the night, closed his eyes, and waited.

Workshops: **Memoir/Autobiography**

This section includes short pieces written by members in advance of a workshop on Memoirs/Autobiography writing, which was led by Sheena Munro.

Topics could be chosen from themes such as a friend/relative, a schoolteacher, a place, a pet, a building, an amusing memory, a hobby, any of which might well be a chapter in their memoir.

The suggestion was that they might consider making this the theme of a whole book, as an alternative to writing a complete autobiography. So the finished memoir might be, for example 'Books that have influenced me' (or even 'changed my life').

We looked at one or two examples of memoir writing by local writers and considered what made them effective. We then shared pieces written for the workshop and spent some time expanding the topic into a piece that might be submitted for the group's anthology, as a preliminary to embarking on a book.

Pam Macintyre

My Grandfather
Jenny Fyfe

I never knew my grandfather, and what I heard about him from my mother did not encourage me to like him. If I were to meet him now, I doubt if I would find him a kindred spirit. I do, however, find him an interesting and admirable character.

This man, John Burleigh, was born into a degree of poverty barely imaginable to his affluent descendants of today. His single mother was a farm servant. She had previously been married to a James Lauder and had other children with him but had been alone for several years. John seems to have been especially precious to her even though she had some difficulty in deciding what surname he should go by. Mostly he was known as John Burley or

Burleigh, but on at least one occasion she stated that his father was James Lauder. However that was clearly impossible: the dates don't fit. On several official documents she listed his father as Archibald Arnot, a possibly fictitious name, and John as John Burley Arnot. No matter how precious he was, poverty forced his mother to send him to work as a weaver at the age of eight.

At thirteen, he exchanged weaving for coal mining. With virtually no education, he managed in spite of a sixteen-hour work day to study by himself to such effect that when he finally achieved university entrance he was ahead of his fellow students in Latin, Greek and Mathematics. After graduation first in Arts and then in Theology, he became a Free Church minister in Blantyre.

Apparently he was assiduous with his ministerial duties, but that was not enough for him. He became a wealthy man through buying property and renting it either for housing or workshops. The proceeds were spent not so much on himself and his family as on various good works. For example, he set up a free evening school for working men at his own expense. Some of his activities were carried out in co-operation with a friend who was a Roman Catholic priest, unusual in a town where sectarian strife was strong.

He died suddenly at the age of seventy-two, still in rather more than would be considered as full-time work today. The local papers described his funeral as attended by so many people of every religious denomination that the church was not big enough for them and the surrounding streets too were full of mourners.

Last year I went to visit his grave for the first time and found it had been vandalised, along with sixty other graves, by a group of teenaged boys, some of them perhaps the great grandsons of the miners who had been a special concern of Rev. John Burleigh in his ministerial days.

The Window

Jo Mulkerrin

I watch my mother as she stands looking out of the large lounge window of the house on Kilburn Lane. I watch with her, and what we see is typical of the afternoon life of the street. Opposite is Mr Kalakroni's café with its grubby ice cream blind bearing the weight of earlier rainfall. Customers are few, and Mr K sits outside smoking. Schoolgirls from St Luke's wander casually arm in arm, turning home down Second Avenue. Two boys sit on the pavement rolling marbles along the gutter, and the No.36 buses queue up, ready to head off across the city at their appointed time.

Her left arm is supporting her ample bosom, her hand clutching hard a handful of lilac jumper. On her right hand she wears her amethyst engagement ring, which she uses to tap on the window. She sings brightly, desperately, her body tense, jigging from foot to foot.

"Mademoiselle from Armentières, parlez-vous …"

She taps out the rhythm with the ring, making a sharp staccato sound, on to the end of the song.

"Inky pinky parlez-vous."

As she sings, she watches and waits for something to engage her, offer her something to fill the void, comfort her sad and sorry psyche. Down at the end of the road, outside The Falcon Hotel, Darkie is shouting his relentless mantra –

"News an' Standard; News an' Standard…"

I watch her. She looks like a solitary bird, fluttering at the window, trying to find a way out.

*

When I am at the window, it is dark and I duck down beneath the ledge. At the age of eleven, I am filled with my own anxiety; I am very much my mother's daughter. I believe the noise I hear from the street at night is the tramp of Nazi soldiers who have conquered London and are annexing Kilburn Lane.

Fear is coupled with exhilaration as all the stories I have been fed overrun my tired mind. It won't be until 40 years later that I discover that the Household Cavalry use my street to exercise their horses in the quiet of night. When I hear this, I feel exonerated. Not mad after all.

*

Cissy will also stand at this window. She has Down's Syndrome, and my mother is looking after her for the afternoon. Cissy lives with her elderly parents and two older brothers, Eric and Rex, who own the Radio shop over the road. The shop is sandwiched between Mr K's café and The Falcon Hotel. They also have a blind, but theirs is bright and clean, with Rex Radio written on it.

Cissy also jigs from foot to foot to her own internal rhythm. Her unpredictable noises scare me. She cries for her own mother but finds solace in the distraction of the street activity. But she can't see well enough through the thick cotton lace curtain. She scratches at it with her fingers but the view is no clearer. Agitated, she looks into the room and spots my mother's sewing box. In the box is a pair of bright shiny dressmaking shears. With clumsy fingers she wields the shears and cuts a jagged hole in the curtain big enough to see through. Now she can see what everyone else can, and it quietens her.

My mother is very angry, bursts into tears and shouts at Cissy. Cissy is now sobbing – great heaving sobs, and her movements become uncontrolled. I watch from the top of the stairs. My mother telephones Rex Radio and Eric is dispatched to collect Cissy. I watch at the window as he hurries across the road to rescue his sister from my mother's unreliable care.

Special Summer Memories

Judy Harvey

It was the summer of 1952, a flourishing, hopeful time in America. It had been a long adjustment for many of the soldiers who had served their country during a terrible world war. The lucky ones were settled into family life and had a civilian job. There was even a prospect of buying one's own home, a dream of so many. The government provided ex-soldiers with low interest financial help called the GI Bill.

My dad worked in the egg business. He had a large warehouse where they candled eggs by hand. He also had a small store in the city of Chicago, in which he sold his eggs and chickens. I used to go with him on Saturdays and was fascinated to watch the ladies hold each egg in front of a light to check that no chicks were inside. I loved to feed the chickens and check for eggs.

On the way home we would stop for a rainbow ice cream cone. Not just any cone but one that was made of seven flavors. Each one was carefully layered onto the cone by a flat shovel scoop. They cost 50 cents and were fabulous.

My mother was a housewife. We lived on the third floor of an apartment building on the south side of Chicago. The back door opened on to a connecting porch that then opened up into my grandparents' apartment.

My favorite thing to do was to sneak into Grandma's kitchen and pinch a bite off a freshly made cake or pie and then run quick as a rabbit back into our kitchen.

Then I would hear my grandma say, "There is a mouse in my kitchen and I am going to catch her."

I would go back for another bite and she would catch me and snuggle me against her ample bosom and tell me how much she loved her little mouse.

Weekly, the coal man would come to our building and fill up the coal shoot in the basement. I loved to slide down the new pile of coal and bump along until I reached the bottom. My mother was horrified at my sooty clothes and her 'young lady' acting like a boy. It was just the beginning of me never meeting her expectations!

There were wonderful sounds and interesting people that came with their wares down our alley. A round-faced Polish man came with the ice for my grandmother's refrigerator. He slung the ice over his shoulder with huge silver tongs and then he would climb the three flights of stairs to her back door. She always gave him a cool glass of homemade lemonade and cookies or cake to reward him.

There was a very skinny Negro man with tight curly hair who had a singsong phrase that got everyone down to the alley to buy fruit and vegetables from him. He would sing 'Strawberries' over and over. You never wanted to miss them. They were big and juicy and didn't need any sugar. He always called us 'chillen'. Mother said it was how Negros talked and he meant 'children'. We liked him because he always gave us a peach or apple.

Mother and Dad took us for a ride in our new car one Sunday. We went out to the suburbs to see model homes. To our great surprise, Mother and Dad bought one. They even let me pick the color. Yellow. We planned to move in the end of the summer, just before school started. It was an amazing thing to think we would live in our own house. My parents were very proud and excited.

Two weeks before we were to move, my brother and I came down with mumps. It was an especially hot summer and mind you, we did not have air-conditioning. We were miserable. My brother cried and cuddled up to me in my four-poster bed, which made us both sweat. My mother had an electric fan going and tried all kinds of things to soothe us but nothing worked, not even ice cream.

My grandpa came to the rescue. He had white hair and an engaging smile that made his eyes twinkle when he laughed. He smoked a Meerschaum pipe with heavenly smelling tobacco. He strung a piece of twine from one post to the other at the foot of my bed. Then he made wonderful characters out of his pipe cleaners and the paper wrappers from my grandma's box of candy.

Before our eyes he created a charming circus. The animals hung onto the twine. Then he made dips and creases in our bedclothes and created a circus parade. It was magical.

For our final and best treat, Grandpa took out his violin and played lovely music for us. The music was mesmerizing and my brother and I went fast asleep.

Before long, we were better and helping Mother pack boxes for our big move. The closer we got to the actual moving date, the more anxious I felt. I became very uncooperative and spent lots of time with my grandparents. I had such mixed feelings. I was happy and secure with my life as it was. Yet our new yellow house, my own room, a new school, and new friends all seemed like a great adventure. Only time would tell.

Of Otters and an Author

Pamela Macintyre

I nearly burst with excitement when the invitation came to visit Gavin Maxwell's house at Sandaig with my parents. Reading *Ring of Bright Water* had filled my impressionable thirteen-year-old mind with romantic notions of otters frolicking in tumbling burns. My father had arranged for the author's huge sand-coloured Land Rover, with Arabic script painted in white on sides and back, to be repaired at short notice in Inverness. Our visit was a favour returned.

After a long and nauseating journey we arrived at a lay-by south of Glenelg. Soon an engine labouring in low gear could be heard and from over a bank on the seaward side of the road, lurched a battered, open-sided Army jeep driven by a boiler-suited young man with dark floppy hair. This was Jimmy Watt who lived at Sandaig. He wasn't very talkative. Clambering into the back of the jeep we perched on bare metal seats. There was a pungent smell of petrol as we bucked and leapt down the roughest of tracks over a steep hillside at a snail's pace until Sandaig came into view. The house, with a zigzag of wooden outbuildings adjoining the south side, sat facing away from the sea on a large sandy promontory. It was whitewashed with three dormer windows at the front, and a porthole window high up on the north side.

Our host, older, thinner and more hunched than I had imagined, looked quite sinister behind dark sunglasses despite the dull day. He shook us firmly by the hand and invited us inside. I was struck by the smell of pitch pine, peat smoke and men's sweat. An entry in my diary reads, 'This is not a horrible smell but very enchanting' and 'a dark main room crammed full of all sorts of things'. The walls were lined with shelves full of tins and driftwood, small paintings of sea scenes, ceramic plates painted with animals and birds, and a game trophy or two. Bookshelves shouldered the empty open fireplace, above which a heavy stone lintel bore the engraved Latin inscription 'Non fatuum huc persecutus ignem', which means 'it is no Will of the Wisp that I have followed here'. A large fully rigged wooden yacht perched on a shelf above looked poised to set sail on the seas outside.

I sank into heavy soft cushions on a long low sofa and felt immediately at home. Tea was offered and readily accepted. The thought of tea soon had me squirming in my seat until I plucked up courage to ask. I was shown to a tiny lavatory off the main room. My diary records 'the lavatory has envelopes with exotic stamps Sellotaped all over the walls and doors. It is very interesting.' I was tempted to linger but didn't want to miss the talk next door. A book about Slimbridge brought on a recent visit by Peter Scott was being handed round.

Without warning, Gavin Maxwell turned his attention to his youngest guest, me. He didn't say much as we filed through Jimmy Watt's sleeping quarters to Edal the otter's enclosure. She had a large pool to herself and seemed delighted to see two of her favourite people. She chittered excitedly, standing on her hind legs scolding for food, catching the sand eel lobbed at her effortlessly in her paws. With full attention concentrated on despatching it, her whiskers twitched rather sweetly in contrast to the display of lethal teeth. She was a beautiful otter, her white front showing up best when floating on her back. Streamlined, dainty and intelligent, it was no wonder her fans loved her.

"We'll go upstairs to see Teko without disturbing him. We can't keep Edal and Teko together any more. They fight," explained our host leading us to his low-ceilinged, simply furnished quarters at the north end of the house. I was urged to clamber over the blue counterpane and look through the recessed porthole in the gable end that I had seen from the jeep. Below was another enclosure where Teko was standing at the edge of a rectangular pool. A larger otter of a different species to Edal, he played and gambolled happily by himself, quite oblivious of me. With that, it was time to leave and as the jeep climbed the hill at a crazy angle I was already brimming with happy memories.

I wrote to Jimmy Watt to thank him. At least that's what I told myself. My diary records that I was in love with him and I spent an impatient few weeks waiting for his reply. He didn't need to, of course. But he did. He sent me a post card and I still have it.

Three years later in 1968 the house at Sandaig burned down and Edal perished in the fire. Cooped up in my school prison, I wrote a mournful letter to Gavin Maxwell who had moved to the remote island of Eilean Ban, which today supports part of the Skye Bridge. To my surprise I received a charming and thoughtful reply. I could even smell the peat smoke on the paper it was written on. I imagined him alone by a roaring fire writing letters with his sepia ink fountain pen on his lighthouse island. I have treasured his letter to this day.

At seventeen my ambition to live alone on the west coast of Scotland was undoubtedly fuelled by my visit to Sandaig, and by reading Gavin Maxwell's books. My headmistress was not impressed with my plans for the future and gave me a stern talking to. It was years before I forgave her.

I still have those books today, two of them signed copies, and in one he wrote my name – in sepia ink, of course. Although the books are no longer central to my life, in a way I have fulfilled one childhood dream. I do live by the sea now, and the joy that brings is all I hoped it would be.

The Gaucho Fair: Buenos Aires's best kept secret

Freda Bassindale

In the early evening sunshine the street had atmosphere, a smell of decay, and an aura of excitement. We followed the music to a tree-lined square and listened to the haunting sounds of the female singer and her accompanying musicians. We strolled past stalls selling jewellery, crafts, clothing, books, prints and other tempting items. We sat at an outdoor bar and ordered a cold beer. As the evening wore on, young and old began to dance: they danced with a fervour and passion that was a joy to watch.

The Argentine tango began in the late 19th century, in the lower-class districts of Buenos Aires. Here, on the periphery of the city, in bars, cafés and courtyards, the ordinary men and women enacted their problems, their memories and their city, in this sensual, alluring dance.

The Feria de Mataderos promised 'an awesome sight' according to a small snippet in the website of the Buenos Aires City Tourist Association, 'featuring live music and dancing, great food and horsemen galloping through the streets.' How could we resist? We soaked up the atmosphere and looked forward to the galloping gauchos.

As we mingled with the crowds, my friend and I realised that we were the only foreigners present. Tall, fair-skinned and much too well-dressed, we were very conspicuous. People stared, and several times we heard the word 'forastero': stranger. As darkness fell, the crowd swelled and became much more vociferous. The music increased in tempo and volume and suddenly the atmosphere was no longer relaxed. We felt apprehensive.

The night before, having had dinner in an outdoor restaurant in the upper class San Telmo district of Buenos Aires, the manager insisted on phoning for a taxi to convey us back to our hotel.

"It is not safe for two ladies," he said. "Lots of bad people about." Now, here we were, in a run-down area on the very edge of Buenos Aires, surrounded by people who were, if not exactly bad, certainly not too friendly. We decided to look for a taxi.

The main road was tree-lined and poorly lit. We realised that during our time at the feria, we had not seen a single policeman. Nor were there any taxis plying their trade. This was a poor residential district with no shops or bars where we might ask to use the phone. After an anxious wait, a taxi hove into view carrying a single passenger. We ran down the street after it until it came to a stop. Even before it disgorged its passenger, we had negotiated its hire back to Buenos Aires city centre. As we climbed into its shabby interior, we heard a yell and the sound of many pounding hooves. The gauchos were on their way, but because of our feeble fears, the show would have to go on without us.

Toys and a Special Christmas

Helen Jackson

It was Christmas 1959. I was ten years old and still anxious to see what 'Santa' had brought me!

Being the second oldest of eight children, Christmas had for many years been fairly low key with any small gifts gratefully appreciated, this being due to the post-war years and a large family of children to be attended to. Many families were in similar circumstances, so it did not seem odd.

My mother was fully engaged in looking after the home and family, and father had been in various low-paid jobs since leaving the army after his National Service had been completed. So money was tight for many years, but recently Dad had got a 'good job' in a factory and Granny Mac was still doing her share of knitting for all of us and also providing some added help at these special times.

What would we get this year? My sisters and I shared a bedroom and we all hoped for something special as we were now growing up with me ten, Ann nine, and Margaret eight.

What surprises awaited us!

I got a school desk and chair – it was fantastic! A whole piece of furniture, just for me. It had a lid which, when lifted, provided enough space for all my 'special' things – at this time that would have been books, pens, pencils and writing paper. I was the academic one in the family with high hopes of doing well in the 11+ exam and going on to the High School.

What about Ann? She got a bus conductress's outfit, complete with the machine to issue bus tickets and a pouch for collecting the fares. She was well pleased and spent all day charging everyone for coming up the stairs into our house.

And then Margaret, what was her present? A nurse's outfit, with the uniform to dress up in as well as all the equipment to take our blood pressure, stethoscope to sound all our chests and, her favourite, a needle to administer those hated injections. She had fun that day making sure we were all healthy and prescribing lots of injections, especially for our brothers.

How had Santa known what effect these toys would have on our respective futures?

I became a teacher and had lots of desks to compare with my toy one over the years. Ann did spend some of her adult life as a conductress but did not really like the 5am rises the job required. Margaret took up nursing and went on to be involved in the radical changes to come, with regard to looking after those with mental health problems.

Clever Santa! I hope he chooses gifts as carefully for today's children.

Domestic Archaeology

Fran Tilbrook

An article in the *Sunday Herald* stated that Dig It! 2015 would be a festival showcasing archaeology in Scotland, aiming to dispel the notion that archaeology is elitist.

Anyone visiting Cromarty in the summer of 2013 would have needed no such convincing: volunteers of all ages poured in to help the small team of experts excavating a medieval archaeology site next to the Cromarty Firth shoreline.

Excited though I was by that project, I am also intrigued by my own, much humbler domestic archaeological finds – pottery shards – which in my case are relative youngsters - probably no older than about 1850.

Toiling away in our Victorian kitchen garden I often think of the gardeners who worked the soil before we moved here, 39 years ago. What did they grow and where? Who planted the now ancient, once-espaliered fruit trees along the south-facing walls? One old lady in Cromarty, who remembered as a child helping her father in this garden (over 100 years ago) said a donkey used to pull a large roller across the (then) ornamental lawns. It wore special protective 'shoes' to prevent damage to the precious grass. This story conjures up a world where the householders enjoyed the garden and its bounty but never got their hands dirty, were never intimate with the soil as we owner-gardeners are today.

During its 164-year history, our house has seen a succession of owners and tenants come and go, and in the 1960s it was a guest house. So a whole host of people have eaten and slept under its roof. And a clumsy lot they were, forever breaking their crockery, because out there in the garden I'm constantly coming across shard after shard. How do these remnants of tea, coffee and dining sets come to be in the soil?

It's only in the last few years that I've started to gather up the prettiest of these pieces – they intrigue me. I love the small fragments with their intricate patterns, from the most delicate blues to fine burgundy stripes, from cup handles to bits of saucers. It's fun trying to imagine the object it came from, there's such variety out there: from bits of curved white porcelain (possibly the remains of the best teapot?) to utilitarian brown earthenware (perhaps from a pie dish filled with apples from those espaliered trees?). Strangely, nearly all the fragments are different from each other, so any hopes of eventually piecing together a cup, plate or serving dish are slim. It's a fascinating business, however, collecting, washing and sorting the pieces, wondering about their provenance and when in the house's long history they each found their way into our vegetable patch and flower borders.

Before there were household waste collections, and centuries after the medieval shell middens uncovered by the Cromarty Community Archaeology Project, people were still dumping, burying or burning their non-compostable rubbish, scattering the ashes somewhere away from the house – an early form of landfill but far more benign than today's tonnes of polluting rubbish. Assuming the broken crockery was dumped rather than burnt, how have the shards become so widely distributed in our garden? Perhaps the gardeners used some fragments as crocks to line flowerpots. When the pots were eventually emptied, did they shake the contents, shards and all, over the beds or on to the large compost heaps which were eventually returned to the soil? Or over the years did a succession of remorseful servants beat a furtive path to the garden, clutching in their guilty hands the latest scraps of broken china? If so, why do I only ever turn up individual fragments?

As for their age – how can I date the pieces? I'd love to know if any were likely to have belonged to the Brydens, for example. Colina Bryden and some of her family survived the Siege of Lucknow in 1857, moving to our house in 1873. 'My' old lady (mentioned above) remembered seeing Mrs Bryden's harp in the hall of the house. It too had survived the rigours of the Siege and of being repatriated to Scotland. Did the family bring their best china home with them? Is any of that in my collection?

I wonder if anyone has a definitive answer to all these questions? Do other gardeners or archaeologists share this jackdaw-like obsession, thrilled each time they unearth another shard to add to the collection?

It certainly makes digging a more interesting pastime, not

knowing what I'll find each time, whether the pieces will be plain or patterned, thick or thin, large or small. But I may be coming to the end of this 'domestic archaeology'. A recurring back problem, together with the 'no dig' mantra from The Soil Association, mean that in future the beds may lie undisturbed, compost and mulches laid on the surface rather than dug in. Increasingly, it'll be up to the rain, moles or worms to reveal any remaining buried treasure.

So it's time to do something with the shards, to acknowledge their link with the house that has been so much a part of our family's life. The grandchildren and I will together make mosaics to adorn some of the walled garden walls. One thing's for certain: the remaining fragments won't be consigned to the bin for a second time, this time ending up in landfill hundreds of miles away. Perhaps I should dig the remainder back into the beds for future domestic archaeologists to discover, ponder over and treasure.

Mental

Pam Macintyre

Right, 3A – mental arithmetic. Get your jotters out," said Miss S, her piercing blue eyes huge behind her spectacles. "Come along now," she sensed the reluctance.

The heavy, worn desk lids slowly rose in salute and, with a faint rustle, slim red-covered jotters appeared. A pencil dropped and earned the culprit a glare. "Quietly with those desk lids," barked Miss S, addressing us all.

I was awash with dread. Miss S began, repeating each question twice, using her deliberate, slightly posh accent. The first few questions I could manage, although I still had to count up the answers on my fingers, but the questions about speed and time and eggs in baskets soon had me leaving blank spaces on most lines. I was no good at mental arithmetic, and anxiety and panic seemed to confirm how useless I was. I fidgeted in my seat in the middle row.

Starting from the front of the class each pupil gave their answer. I couldn't resist a nervous glance at my neighbour's jotter, and before I knew it Miss S strode up the aisle and rapped me over the knuckles with her ruler. "No cheating." She towered above me, her fleshy jowls and tight grey perm quivering. I blushed hotly with pain, guilt and fear, struggling to hold back the tears.

Still, I should be glad that I hadn't talked in class, which could earn a spell standing in the dark corridor outside the classroom. Some of the boys were given the strap for insolence. Oh, where was nice Miss P from the reception class, or even Mrs F in 2A, who seemed so scary at the time!

It wasn't until ten years later that a kind, patient Mrs M helped me solve the mysteries of mental arithmetic, and to her I am eternally grateful.

Royal Stars in our Eyes

Sheena Munro

2014 – Seven hundred years on from Bannockburn, and Scotland, it seems, is once again ettling for the freedom to govern its own affairs, and break up the Kingdom of which James VI and I had happily accepted the crown in 1603. 'Jamie the Saxth' was not a glamorous figure, and yet the Stewart line into which he was born did provide Great Britain with a focus for the obsession with 'celebrity' which seems to be a permanent part of our national psyche. His mother, Mary Queen of Scots, was beautiful, talented and tragic. Like Mary, her grandson Charles lost his head and remains a sad and lonely figure. England briefly embraced Republicanism, but the charmless Oliver Cromwell could not compete in the celebrity stakes, and Scotland surprisingly led the way in welcoming the return of Royalty in the person of the Merry Monarch, Charles II, who well understood the need for love and laughter, music and celebration in the lives of his subjects. Another Charles was to earn his place in the parade of 'glamorous royals' in 1745-6. Curiously, it was once more in Scotland that he made his mark, leaving a litany of popular songs and a portrait to grace countless shortbread tins. Thereafter, the Scottish fascination with lost Stewart causes faded into oblivion until Walter Scott persuaded a Hanoverian king to don the tartan, and the royals helped to create a new romantic image for 'Caledonia stern and wild'.

Sixty-two years ago, not quite seven years after the end of World War Two, Winston Churchill, who had inspired us in our darkest days, voiced the romantic notion of a 'new Elizabethan age'. Doubtless the war leader turned statesman hoped this was the start of a return to greatness for a country still suffering from a degree of austerity. He understood the need for glamour in our lives, and the build-up to the coronation of an attractive though serious-minded young woman with a dashing prince consort seemed the ideal focus for optimistic patriotism.

In my teen years (although in fact the term 'teenager' did not then exist), we were of course aware of film stars, though mainly through direct experience of the cinema on a Saturday afternoon.

And theirs was a celluloid world: newspaper or magazine photographs of our heroes and heroines were relatively unusual and always black and white. Photographs of the new Queen, her handsome husband and her delightful little children did however appear with increasing frequency in the newspapers, and young girls like me kept scrapbooks recording the events of the new Elizabethan age and its royal stars.

Newspapers, scissors and paste were all we needed to record our admiration for these people whose world was so far removed from ours, and about whose lives we knew almost nothing. It was an unsophisticated pastime that reflected our lack of experience of 'life'. We had no television and little or no opportunity ever to see these glamorous people in the flesh. Living as I did in Aberdeen, there was a slight chance in the summer time, when the Royal Family, as they must be properly called, with upper case initials, passed through on their way to the annual holiday at Balmoral. At that time, they arrived by train, as Queen Victoria had done, and while there was never an official announcement, we knew that there would be a stopover in Aberdeen Joint Station. So a small crowd of the faithful would gather at the station in the hope of seeing some of the family. They rarely did appear, of course: they were after all on holiday and there would be an official welcome at Ballater station. In 1952, however, there was a treat for the spectators when the then nearly four-year-old Prince Charles and his sister Anne, just short of her second birthday appeared at a window of the train and spent some time observing the crowd. My own undoubted pleasure at seeing them was heightened when I turned round and realised that the girl standing behind me was the Queen's cousin, Princess Alexandra of Kent. One of the station staff told us later that the Kents were in the habit of travelling north by the regular overnight train and enjoying kippers for breakfast at the station restaurant before joining the rest of the family. As a girl of my own age, Alexandra was something of a heroine to me, and it amuses me now to remember that what impressed me about her appearance, apart from her porcelain complexion, was the dark brown trench coat she was wearing –

perhaps her school uniform. Certainly it would not mark her out as a future fashion icon today.

This very low-key but rather charming 'celebrity encounter' was in extreme contrast to the security-hedged, paparazzi-infested public appearances of the famous today. Clichés like 'It was a more innocent age' tend to leap off the keyboard: certainly I, like my contemporaries, was less street-wise than my grandchildren are today. The devotion inspired by the young Elizabeth II never developed into sycophantic adulation. As children eventually became teenagers, they found new idols in the worlds of sport and pop music, and the 'royals' lost much of their star status together with the mystique that had formerly surrounded them. They compete with today's celebrities only in the prurient fascination with their private lives. And yet Queen Elizabeth has survived it all and enjoys the respect and affection of many. It will be interesting to see how far this head of a dysfunctional family may influence the threatened break-up of her 'disunited kingdom'.

Ginger Fizz

Lynn Valentine

One eye glared at me. The other was hidden beneath his hat. He was snuggled into my nephew's chest, coolly giving me the once over to see if I would match up to being a Great-Aunt.

A curl of red hair peeked out from beneath the hat, claiming him as one of ours, the ginger gene still going strong down the decades. Mine had long been denied with hair dye, distancing myself as a cool blonde. The same distancing I'd done with my family, moving away to London as soon as I'd gotten the chance.

"Here, you hold him, Auntie Lynn, have a shot." My nephew Craig held out wee Aulay to me but I wasn't ready for this yet. If I took him I'd carry him out of the house, run down the street and kidnap him. One of those mad women you read about in the papers stealing babies from hospitals. I knew their desperation, that ache in the gut when a friend announced she was pregnant or when happy mums marched past with their children in town.

"Och no, I'm scared I would break him, he looks happy where he is. You know I'm only good with dogs."

Craig laughed but we both knew I was covering up. "Listen, I'll make some tea, Craig, while you look after the wee man. It's still two sugars, right?"

I spent a good five minutes making the tea, calming myself down a bit, ready to face things again.

Craig wandered through to the kitchen with Aulay in his arms. "We were thinking you were lost Auntie Lynn, weren't we Aul?" Aulay looked up at his Dad and gave a wee gurgle.

"No, never lost, just went away for a bit. But I'm back now and I'll see this one growing up." I curled my finger round Aulay's tiny hand and smiled at him. I swear he smiled back.

Workshops: **Humour**

Making people laugh is a difficult task. What tickles one person's funny bone doesn't necessarily have the same effect on another as humour is very much an individual and subjective topic. In this workshop, a number of different types of humour were explored and hints given on how to connect with the reader. Some basic rules (from an individual perspective) were offered and examples of what a few of the participants felt was funny for them were read or discussed. Prior to the event, the group was asked to write something funny about a serious subject chosen from neutering/ spaying cats or dogs, diplomatic immunity or wind farms. Some excellent and original responses were read and a few are included in this anthology, together with a mixture of writing from the workshop and afterwards.

Jeremy Price

A letter from Dulcie
Sheena Munro's outraged pet cat

Dear Jeremiaow Purrice,
   Having purrused your recent emiaowl on the subject of 'humour', I was purrturbed by the invitation to Black Isle Writers to write *humiaowrously* on the subject of 'spaying cats'. Leaving aside the undoubted vulgarity of language, the purrversity of the theme was such as to make a lady purrspire with horror; and the implications, were such a pussillanimiaows policy to be widely purrpetrated, are purrnicious in the extreme. To purge the world of our beautiful, intelligent and quite purrfect species – sir, this is the most purrfidious purrsecution! No, Mr Purrice, we are *not* amewsed!

Stitched Up

Lynn Valentine

I was in the kitchen sniffin' ma bum
When I heard a loud shout "Come, Bruno, come."
Was it time for walkies or mebbe some grub
Or ear and pork scratchins doon at the pub?
I ran to the hall as fast as I could.
Ma she-human said "you're awfully good."
She clipped on ma lead and patted ma head,
I licked her hand but ma heart filled wi dread.
She had on her perfume, Eau de Paris.
She never wore that when walkin' with me.
The last time she had that she'd dropped me off
At kennels, and me, withoot any cough.
I refused to budge but she pulled me oot
And hurled me intae the tiny car boot.
I howled and moaned wi ma ears pinned right back
As the car made its way bumpin' the track.
Well we passed the kennels and ma heart leapt.
It soon shrank doon when we got tae the vet.
I was ta'en into the wee scary room
That smelt o deid dogs and hearts full o gloom.
The vet smiled kindly but gied me a jag.
I woke up much later tied tae a bag.
Worse than that tho was a pain doon below.
I took a wee look and there was the blow.
I wiz no longer top dog runnin wi bitches –
All I hud noo wiz plenty o stitches!

When Winnie Met Paddy

Russell Turner

Paddy: Winnie! Winnie! Over here!

Winnie: Paddy? Jeez – Paddington Bear! Long time no see. How ya doin', bro?

Paddy: Remarkably fine, old chap. I didn't expect to find the great Pooh in London for at least another year. How's Tinseltown?

Winnie: Just crazy. My guys are tyin' up a three-movie deal with Disney so it's no place for a bear who don't wanna grab an AK47 and climb a tall tower. I left the suits to it and took the red-eye back to the old country to chill for a while.

Paddy: Three films? Marvellous. So you've resolved those little problems?

Winnie: Well, ya know the biz. Tigger wants to play Hamlet, Piglet's actin' even weirder than usual and Kanga won't be in the same room with Roo, but I'll bust a few heads if I have to. We start shootin' in the fall when Eeyore's outta rehab.

Paddy: I'm delighted to hear that, old chap. Delighted. There'll be premiere tickets for me and Mrs P, I trust?

Winnie: Sure thing, bro. But look at you – Armani duffel-coat, Gucci suitcase – lookin' *very* sharp.

Paddy: I certainly can't complain, even after The Talent takes his cut.

Winnie: Goddam authors. They're nothin' without us.

Paddy: As you say, old boy. In fact, I'm just popping over to Television Centre for a script conference on the Christmas special. We're still casting for the narrator too – dear Michael was such a hard act to follow – but the BBC tell me that Johnny Depp is extremely keen.

Winnie: Nice work, bro.

Paddy: Indeed, but not everyone is doing so well.

Winnie: Aw heck. Don't tell me Sooty's back on the juice. What is it with that guy?

Paddy: All guilt. He's not been the same since he fired Matthew.

The Corbetts made him, but all he thinks about is the big time in America.

Winnie: Don't tell me about it. "How'd ya do it, Pooh?" he kept askin'. "What's the secret?" Ya can't shut him up when he's full of scotch. "Crazy luck," I told him. "Forget it. You're better off bein' a big fish in a small pond." No offence, bro.

Paddy: None taken, old chap.

Winnie: But would he listen? Naw. "Izzy wizzy let's get busy" might go down a storm with the Brits but on the other side of the pond it's a frost. So how'd the broad take it?

Paddy: I regret to say that he and Soo parted three months ago. It was no surprise.

Winnie: Sweep?

Paddy: Of course. Everyone knew except Sooty.

Winnie: Poor sap. I figure things wadda been a whole lot different if they'd had cubs, but that's pandas for ya. Only interested one day a year and even then nothin' guaranteed.

Paddy: That may be so, but Sweep had no difficulty.

Winnie: The dawg knocked her up? Jeez!

Paddy: Most regrettable. Winnie, it's delightful that our paths crossed but I really must dash. If you'd care to join us tonight, I have assembled the old team to visit our friend in need at his home and offer whatever assistance we can.

Winnie: Sure thing, bro, I'll be there. Us bears gotta stick together. But do me a favour – Yogi, fine; Fozzie, OK; but whatever you do, don't bring that creep Rupert.

Cutting To The Chase

Fran Tilbrook

Scene: A street corner near a park in Glasgow. It's a Monday morning and several dogs are gathering to catch up with any news.

Nip to Griff: You smell different ole pal since you went awa' last week. And whit's wi' that lampshade thing roond yer neck?

Griff: Aw, Nip, dinnae even ask. I'm nae the dog I was, and I'm still no feelin' great.

Nip: How's that?

Griff: Och, I dinnae want to talk aboot it. It's kinda awkward – but well – I s'pose yous'll all goanie find out soon enough.

Nip: Find out what? [*Barks to the other dogs*] Hey guys, awa' over an' hear this!

Griff: OK, OK, watch yersel's! It's still sair doon there.

Fifi: Aw, have you been in an accident, Griff?

Griff: No exactly, Feef, it's kinda embarrassin', what my folks did tae me.

Fifi: Embarrassin'? You mean that collar?

Griff: Naw, no that. That's tae stop me licking my cojones.

Fifi, [*observantly*]: But Griff, where are your cojones?

Griff: Aye, well, you've cut straight to the chase, Feef. That's it. They're gone. Snip, snip, end of.

Dogs: Nah! Jings! Get away! Help ma boab!

Griff: Mind when I went awa' and yous all thought I was on holiday? Well, it wasnae like that.

Nip: Griff? Your voice sounds kinda different – more like Isla's.

Griff: Naw! Yer reckon? Hell, then that's a' part o' the same story.

Dogs: What story, Griff?

Griff: Ah wish it could be one o' they 'Once upon a time' stories, but it isnae. Long story short: ma folks grabbed me and took me alang to the vets [*dogs all do a sharp intake of breath*] and I'm 'you know whatted'. Just like that. A punishment for what I done wi' that gorgeous bitch, Isla. No askin' me whit I thinks o' this plan, no consultation, no counsellin', and once the dreaded deed was done, no post-traumatic stress aftercare. Just some stitches, this collar and a short rest last week. What d'ya make o' that, pals? I'll never be a Daddy again.

Some of the male dogs: Oh that's terrible, Griff. What are they owners like!

Fifi: We'ell, Griff, I have tae say, it's no all bad.

Male dogs: Uh?

Fifi: Well, we girls dinnae want you guys getting the hots for us whenever it's 'that time'. Now we can just be pals, can't we? Go out on the street unmolested, like.

Griff: But Feef, you were up for it, like Isla, like the other lasses. You left all they messages at the corner lamppost, advertisin' your keenness! I couldnae resist your 'allure'.

Fifi: Oh Griff, that's lovely, but it's be'er like this. Oh and by the way, these others are just kiddin' on. They're all bark and nae bite – if you get ma meanin'.

Griff: Is that right, guys? [*silence*]. Nip? [*silence*]. Boxer? [*shifty eyes*]. Rocky? [*distant look at the horizon*]. How did I no notice that? Must be yer lack of personal groomin' and never goin' to the dog barber's. But, Nip, you're ma best pal. Why did you never let on before?

Nip: Well, it's hardly somethin' to brag aboot, is it? I was 'done' when I was a wean and I cannae mind onything aboot it. Mind, I've been dead envious of you with the lassies, I can tell ya.

[*Other dogs nod in agreement*]

Boxer [*silent till now*]: Aye, Griff, but there's another thing. You'll have to watch yer weight now. We neutrals can pile on the pounds, isn't that right, guys?

[*More silent depressed nodding all round*].

Fifi, [*decisively*]: C'mon – yous all need cheerin' up. Let's visit the lamppost and see whit new messages have come in. Then on to the park and play wi' any lost balls.

[*A pregnant pause*].

Dogs [*in unison*]: Are you taking the pish, Feef?

The Contributors

Freda Bassindale: "Always write about what you know" is good advice. I enjoy writing about my personal experiences and for the past twenty-five years I've been compiling my autobiography. It's a collection of short articles and one day I might get round to having it published.

Julie Christie: When I migrated north to Eilean Dubh, Elizabeth Sutherland, a founding member, kindly invited me to BIW group. Initially, I was apprehensive, as I had never written 'formally' before. However, I was keen to join different groups to find out more about the community and soon was encouraged to write!

Jenny Fyfe: During my academic career at the University of Western Ontario my writing was mainly on historical themes, resulting in the publication of four books and several journal articles. I then moved to the Black Isle where I expanded my repertoire to include fiction and local history, little so far published.

Judy Harvey: I am known as "that American lady in Cromarty" even though I have lived here three years and have settled into a wonderful life. I am active in the Cromarty Writers and Black Isle Writers groups. I love writing and am the owner of the Emporium Bookshop.

Claire Hemsworth: My writing is influenced by my faith and is an expression of my experiences and what I learn through different circumstances. I hope that, in sharing my work, others will be encouraged and inspired in their own life and faith journeys.

Jack Hermiston: Non-fiction within education and press-classroom material, articles, books e.g. *Casebook of Careers Material*, The Banffshire Education Authority. Fiction: *The Call of the Helix* and *They Sailed Time* – both runner up Scot Assoc. Writers' annual novel competition. Sailing articles. Poetry: prose poems illustrated and published as a book.

Helen Jackson joined the Black Isle Writers this year and has not written anything other than academic textbooks in the distant past! Since retiring five years ago, her interests are mainly to write memoirs or stories about her family based on her genealogical research over the past 15 years.

Pam MacIntyre: I moved from Inverness to Fortrose in 2013, and joined the Black Isle Writers shortly thereafter. So far I have found the workshops challenging and other writers encouraging. I'd like to write up family papers, then do more creative writing.

Jo Mulkerrin is a published short story writer. She is currently working on her first novel, set in a London prison, delving into the darker side of people's lives. She finds her inspiration in the stark contrast of her writing with the peace and beauty her current surroundings offer.

Sheena Munro has been writing poetry 'of sorts' since she was about seven. She contributed several poems to *Moods and Memories*, a collection of memoirs by Chris Haxton, a former founder member of the Writers Group. Her own memoir *Bridges in Time* was published in 2012.

Jeremy Price was a journalist in a previous existence and over another career wrote more technical documents, some of which are still national publications. He has had articles published in a number of national magazines and now writes short stories as well as working on two books. He likes dark humour.

Dorrie Robertson grew up in a mining area, and as a young girl was fascinated by the darkness and light, sounds and smells of the mine. She trained as a teacher, a job she loved and has remained close to young people, particularly her grandchildren.

Eleanore Simpson moved to Fortrose in 2010. She mainly writes short stories. Often they have their origins in reality but then her imagination takes over. She is currently working on a history of her family in Moray to pass on to her two children.

Elizabeth Sutherland has published extensively, including 22 books on a variety of subjects, but her first love is fiction. She won the Constable Trophy in 1971 and an Arts Council Book Award in 1977. At present she is working on a second book of Highland Folklore from which the story featured in this anthology is taken.

Fran Tilbrook: I joined Black Isle Writers this year to benefit from the support and encouragement of other writers and the stimulus that the workshops provide. I'd like to do more creative writing after previous non-fiction pieces and editorial work such as *Cromarty – Living by the Sea* (2007).

Evelyn Topp: I've been a member of the group for several years. My main interest is in writing biographical stories about relatives and my own family reminiscences for my children and grandchildren. I also like dabbling in poetry writing.

Russell Turner is a journalist and photographer, author of four-and-a-half unpublished novels and a clutch of short stories. He's also the co-author of photography book *Eilean Dubh – The Black Isle* and sole author of children's book *A Cat Called Tess*. He is editor of the magazine *Black Isle Chatterbox*.   www.russellturner.org

Lynn Valentine: I moved to the Black Isle in 2013. The landscape seemed to unlock a language within me, one of poetry and prose that I hadn't ever used before. So I found myself writing, toiling under the blank gaze of Ben Wyvis. I am still unsure of my words but the need to write has become addictive.

Elizabeth Waters: Regular articles for craft magazines, e.g. *Needlework* and *Stitch with the Embroiderers' Guild*. Booklet for *Vilene*. Several books for the Highland Council, recording memories of life in Ross shire.

Acknowledgements

A big thank you to Judy Harvey, her editorial team of Pam MacIntyre, Jeremy Price, Fran Tilbrook and Russell Turner. Without their efforts this Anthology would not have happened.

Eleanore Simpson